On the
TRAIN
Activity Book

Steve Martin

Illustrated by Putri Febriana

THIS BOOK BELONGS TO:

_____

IVY KIDS

·CONTENTS·

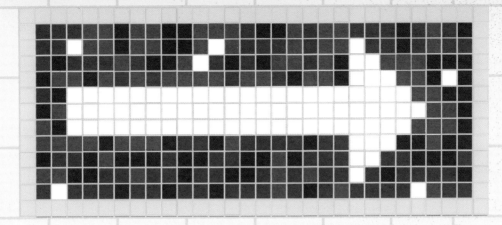

Tickets, Please!

Imagine you're setting off on an exciting rail journey.
There are two important things you need.

First, you need to fill out your travel card.

IF FOUND, PLEASE RETURN TO:

HOME TOWN: _ _ _ _ _ _ _ _ _ _ _

SIGNATURE: _ _ _ _ _ _ _ _ _ _ _

TRAVEL CARD

SURNAME: _ _ _ _ _ _ _ _ _ _ _

FIRST NAME: _ _ _ _ _ _ _ _ _ _ _

DATE OF BIRTH: _ _ _ _ _ _ _ _ _ _ _

Draw a picture of yourself here. There are rules for a travel card photo - no hats, no sunglasses and no smiling!

You also need your train ticket. Fill in the details below. You could copy a real ticket that you have, or you could invent one for an imaginary journey!

DATE: - - - - - - - - - - - - - -

TO: - - - - - - - - - - - - - -

FROM: - - - - - - - - - - - - - -

SEAT RESERVATION: - - - - - - -

JOURNEY TIME: - - - - - - - - - -

TRAIN COMPANY NAME: - - - - - - - - - -

SPOT THE DIFFERENCE

Look at these two busy stations. At first glance they look the same, but there are 10 differences. Draw a circle around each one you find.

FIND THE FREIGHT TRAIN

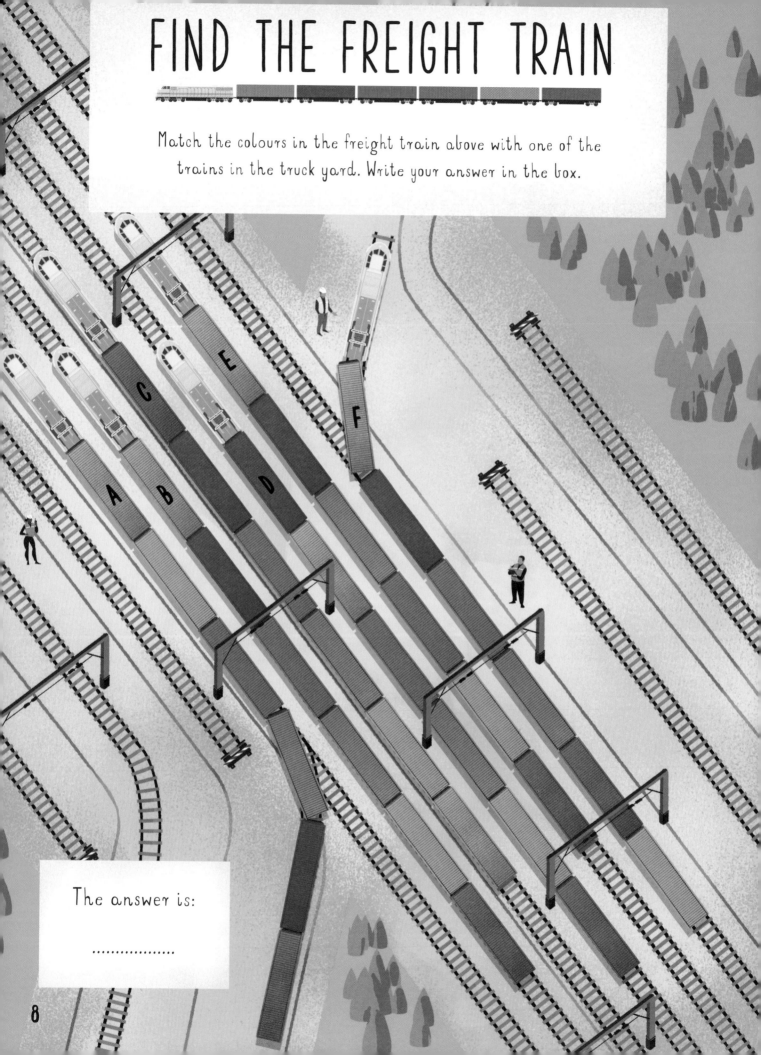

Match the colours in the freight train above with one of the trains in the truck yard. Write your answer in the box.

The answer is:

....

Dot-to-Dot

It's not just trains that travel on tracks. Connect the dots to reveal something else that moves on rails.

Believe It or Not!

Check out these eye-bending questions. You might be surprised by the answers...

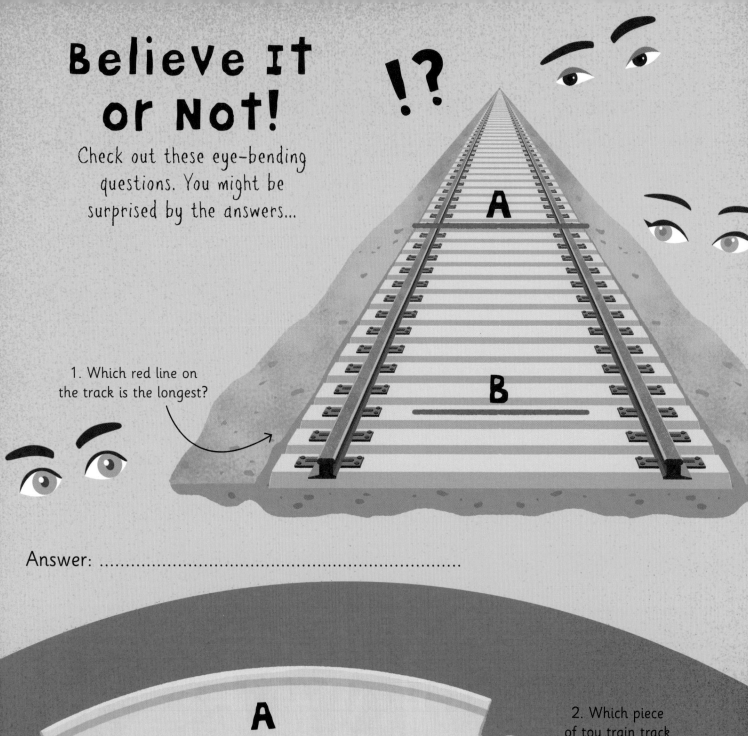

1. Which red line on the track is the longest?

A

B

Answer: ....

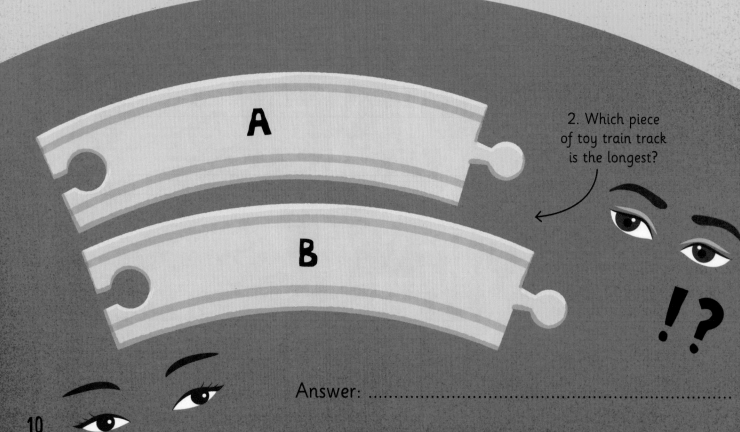

2. Which piece of toy train track is the longest?

A

B

Answer: ....

Faster Than a Speeding Bullet

Can you match the descriptions of these speedy trains to the pictures? Write the name of the train next to its picture.

Shinkansen

This Japanese train is also known as a bullet train because it is super fast. Its design, which includes a long, rounded nose, helps it to reach speeds of 320 kilometres per hour. It is famous for being on time.

The Rocket

The Rocket was built in the UK in 1829. It was famous for its design, which included wooden panels and a tall pipe. It reached a top speed of 58 kilometres per hour, which was very fast at the time.

Flying Scotsman

Trains used to be powered by steam, and sent out clouds of smoke as they travelled. A famous steam train was the Flying Scotsman. In 1934, it became the first train in the UK to reach a speed of 160 kilometres per hour.

1. _____
   _____

2. _____
   _____

3. _____
   _____

Matching Game

These children have taken two train journeys together. By drawing lines between them, can you match each child on the outward journey with the child on the return journey? One has been done for you.

Be careful — they are not wearing the same clothes!

Outward

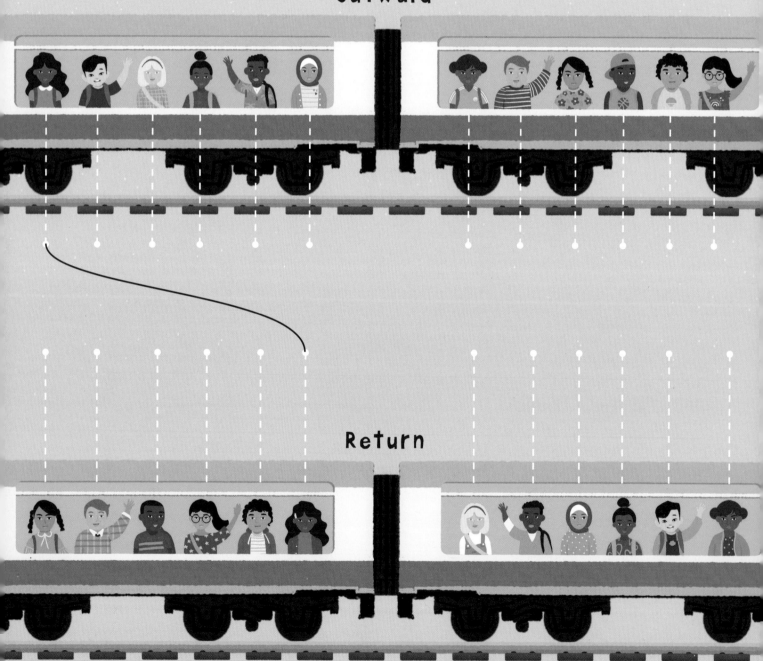

Return

TRAIN, PLANE OR SHIP

Are these safety instructions for train, plane or ship passengers?
Circle the correct answer.

1. Stand away from the edge of the platform.

TRAIN   PLANE   SHIP

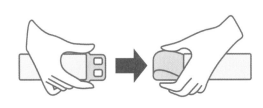

2. Keep your seatbelt fastened during take-off.

TRAIN   PLANE   SHIP

3. Do not go on deck in rough weather.

TRAIN   PLANE   SHIP

4. Do not walk across the track.

TRAIN   PLANE   SHIP

5. Listen carefully when the flight attendant gives a safety talk.

TRAIN   PLANE   SHIP

DESIGN A POSTER

Posters are designed to encourage people to travel by train and visit exciting places.

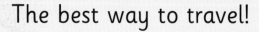

The best way to travel!

VISIT TODAY

Choo choo!

It's your turn to design a travel poster! It can be for the town you live in, somewhere you've visited recently or an imaginary place.

Hidden Train

A picture of a train is hidden in this grid. Colour the squares as listed below to find it. One square has been done for you.

Yellow:
C6, D6, E6, F6, G6, C7, D7, E7, F7, G7, C8, D8, E8, F8, G8, C9, D9, E9, F9, G9

Blue:
I6, J6, I7, J7

Orange:
C1, D1, E1, F1, C2, D2, E2, F2, D3, E3, D4, E4, D5, E5

Green:
A5, B5, A6, B6, A7, B7, A8, B8, A9, B9, A10

Red:
G3, H3, I3, J3, K3, L3, G4, H4, I4, J4, K4, L4, H5, I5, J5, K5, H6, K6, H7, K7, H8, I8, J8, K8, H9, I9, J9, K9

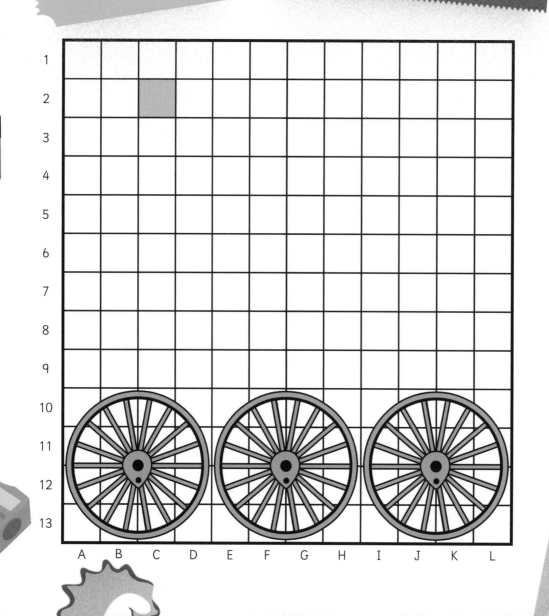

Which Line?

These three trains are full of passengers who want to visit the seaside. But only one train reaches the beach. Which train is it? Write your answer below.

The train that goes to the beach is ......

Picture Sudoku

Imagine you are on a train journey through some beautiful countryside. Here are four sights you might see if you're looking out of the window.

Complete this sudoku picture puzzle. Fill each square with one of the symbols, or you can write the word. Each picture can appear only once in each row, column and mini-grid.

SUBWAY CONUNDRUM

Bea is going to meet her friends – but she doesn't know the name of the subway station she needs to get to. Use the information given to help her find it, crossing out stations as you eliminate them.

- It is not on the blue line.
- It is not on the same colour line as The Mall station.
- It is more than two stops away from Woodland station.
- It does not have the word 'street' in its name.

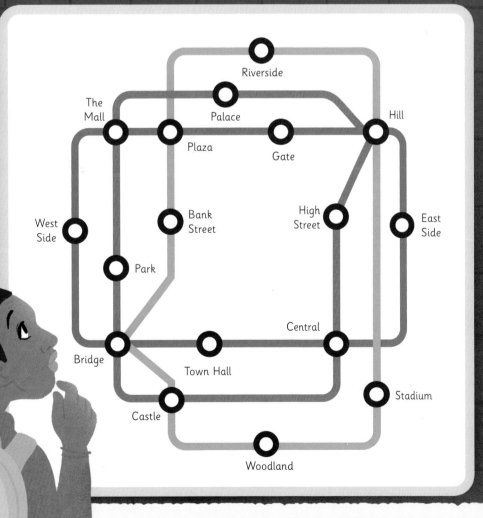

The station that Bea needs to get to is: _____

Colour the Station

This station needs your skills to make it come alive with bright colours! You can use pencils, crayons or felt-tips.

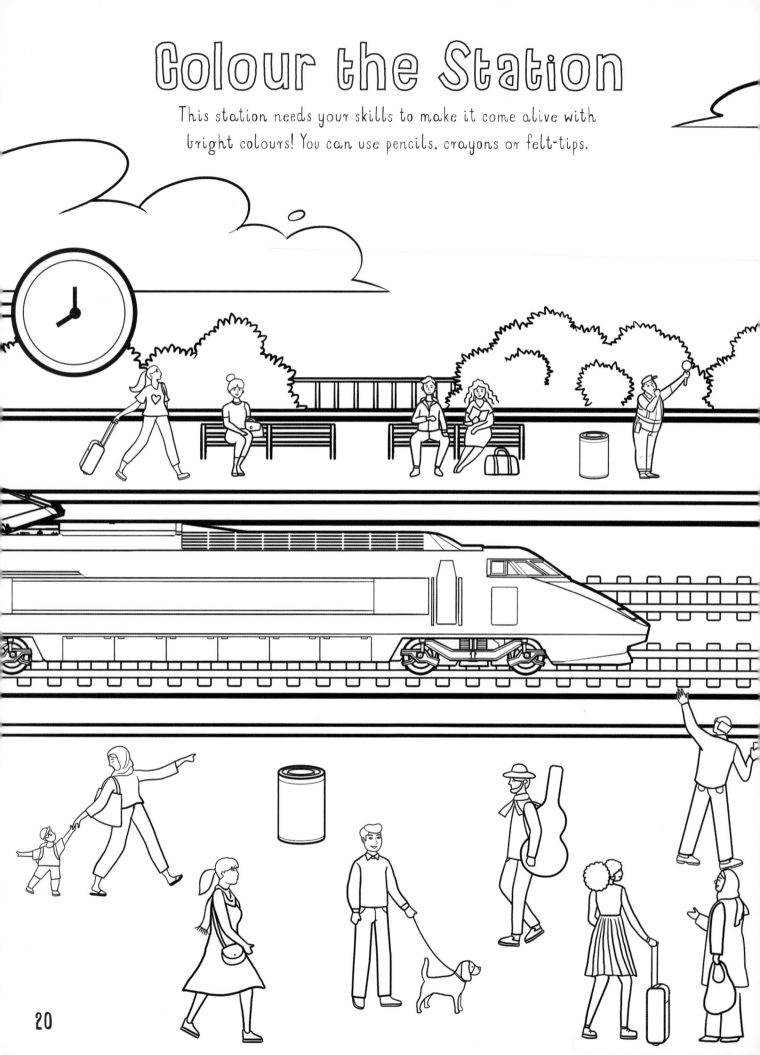

Create a Comic

A train journey can have amazing sights to see!

Oliver has just been on a very exciting trip by train. In each box, draw what he saw along the way.

This was the train that I travelled on.

We passed the sea and I saw a boat sailing in the sunshine.

I saw some mountains that were so high, they had snow on the top.

We passed through a busy town, which had lots of tall buildings.

There was an old castle next to a winding river.

At the end of the journey, we arrived at this station.

Track Puzzle

Can you work out where these four pieces fit in the track?
Write the correct letter in the space next to each missing piece.

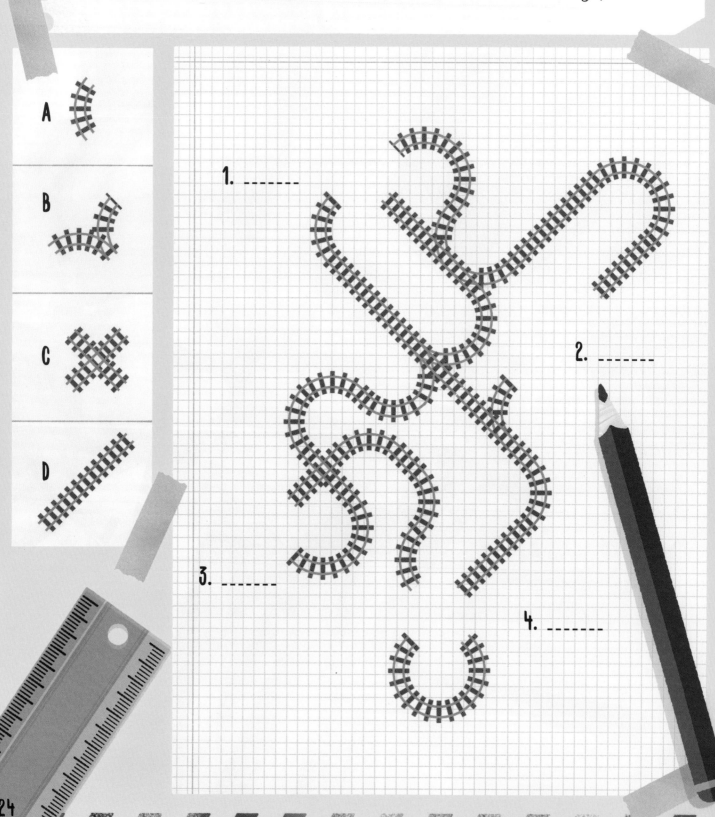

A

B

C

D

1. _____

2. _____

3. _____

4. _____

Train Teasers

Here are some brain-bending riddles for you to solve.
Write your answers in the space provided.

1.

Yesterday, I travelled on a train for 1 hour and 40 minutes. Today, I caught the same train as yesterday. It travelled at the same speed, but the journey took 100 minutes.

How was this possible?

\- \-

\- \-

2.

A dog travelled from New York to Philadelphia at the same speed as the train from New York to Philadelphia.

How was this possible?

\- \-

\- \-

3.

You are driving a train. At the first station, six passengers get on. At the second station, four passengers get on. At the third station, seven passengers get on and three get off.

What colour is the train driver's hair?

\- \-

\- \-

TRUE OR FALSE?

Here are some interesting facts about railways around the world. But are they all real? Tick either the True or False boxes.

1. Russia's Trans-Siberian Railway, which runs from Moscow to Vladivostok, is nearly 4,000 kilometres long.

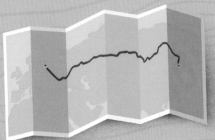

TRUE ☐   FALSE ☐

2. Almost 100,000 people use Tokyo's Shinjuku Station every day.

TRUE ☐   FALSE ☐

3. The Ghan train takes 54 hours to travel between the Australian cities of Darwin and Adelaide.

TRUE ☐   FALSE ☐

Capital Cities

There are trains and train stations in almost every country in the world! Have you ever taken a train in a different country?

Berlin

Tokyo

Beijing

London

Moscow

Paris

Washington, D.C.

France

China

USA

Germany

UK

Japan

Each of the capital cities listed above has a big, busy train station. Draw a line to match the capital city with the country it is in. One of the capital cities is missing its country – can you circle it?

Steam Engine Sketch

Copy the picture of the steam train below onto the grid on the right. Part of it has been done for you. Draw it square by square, using the numbers as a guide. Once you have finished, colour each train using pens or pencils.

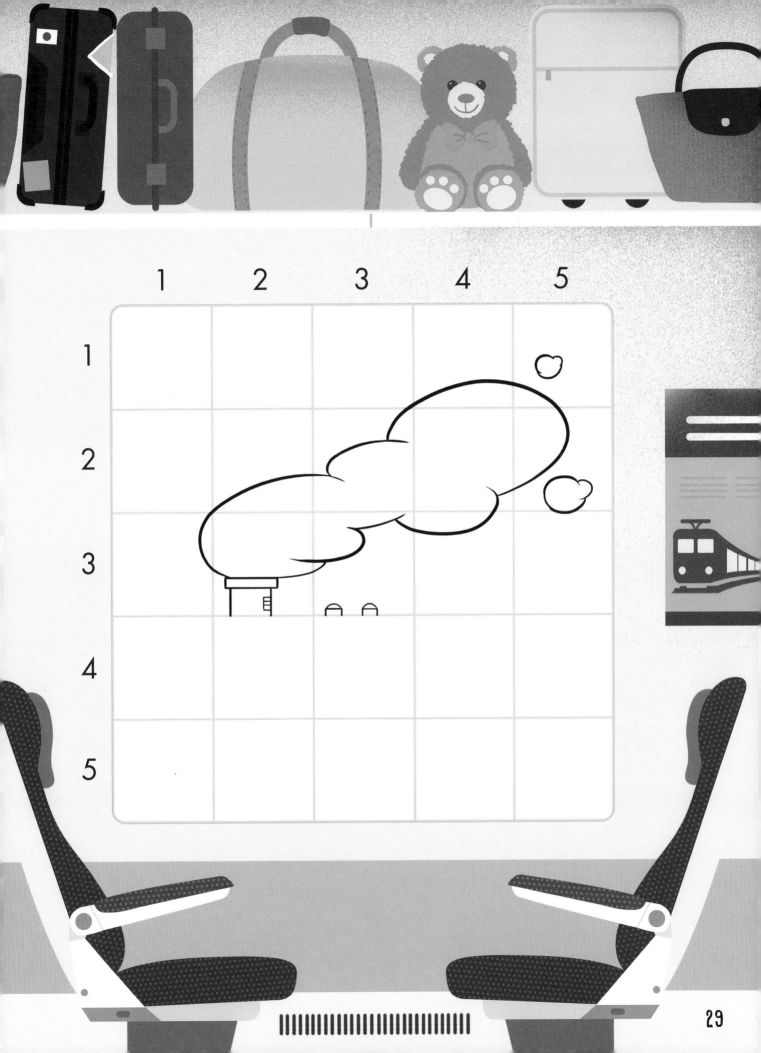

Search the Sleeper

Some rail journeys are so long, the
train has carriages with beds to rest in.
These trains are known as 'sleeper trains'.

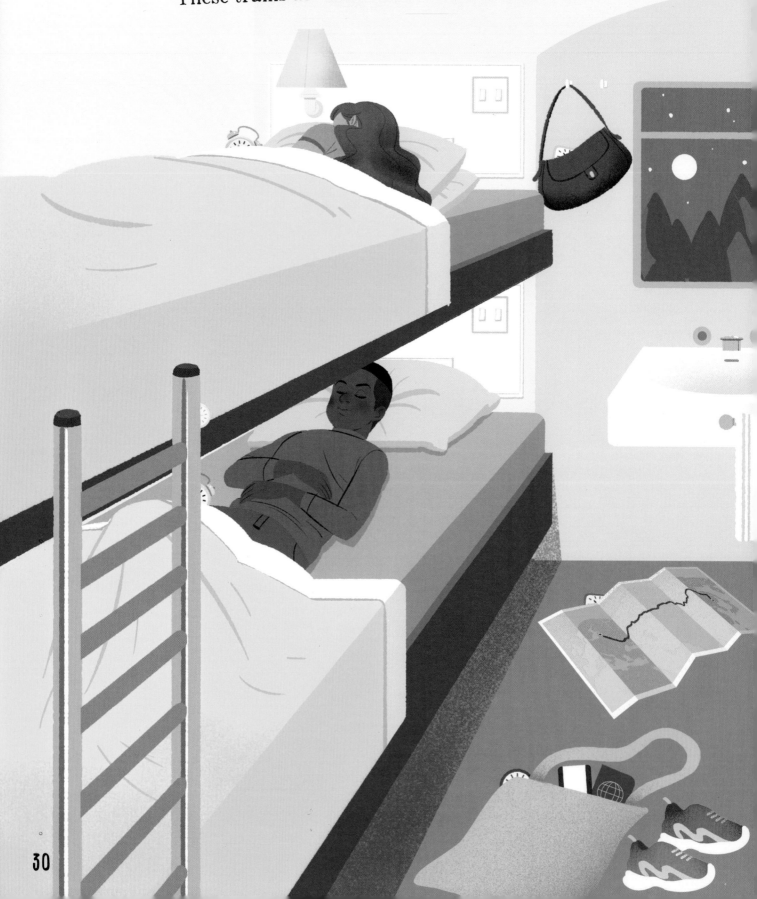

Hamza, Nadia, Billie and Justin are all asleep in their cabin. There are 14 alarm clocks placed around the room to wake them up so that they don't miss their stop. Can you find and circle all of the clocks?

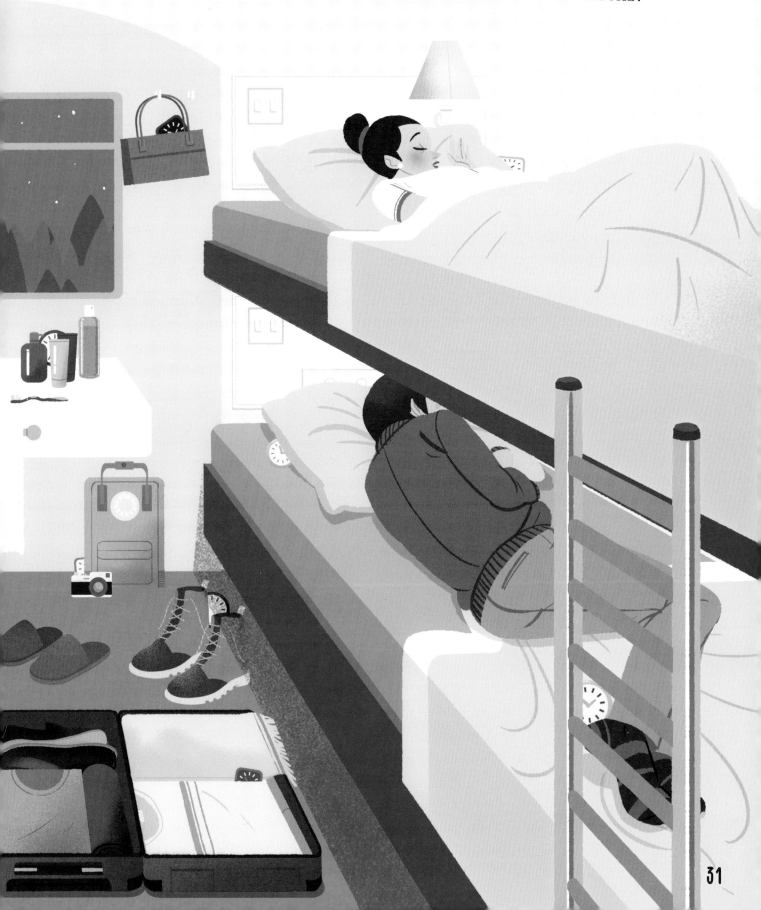

THAT'S NO EXCUSE!

Oh no – a train is delayed! Write a story to explain why it is late, using the pictures at the bottom of the page to help you.

SORRY FOR THE DELAY.
THIS IS BECAUSE...

_____

_____

_____

_____

_____

_____

_____

What's Next?

Study these four sets of patterns. Can you work out which item is next in each list, and draw or write it in the space provided?

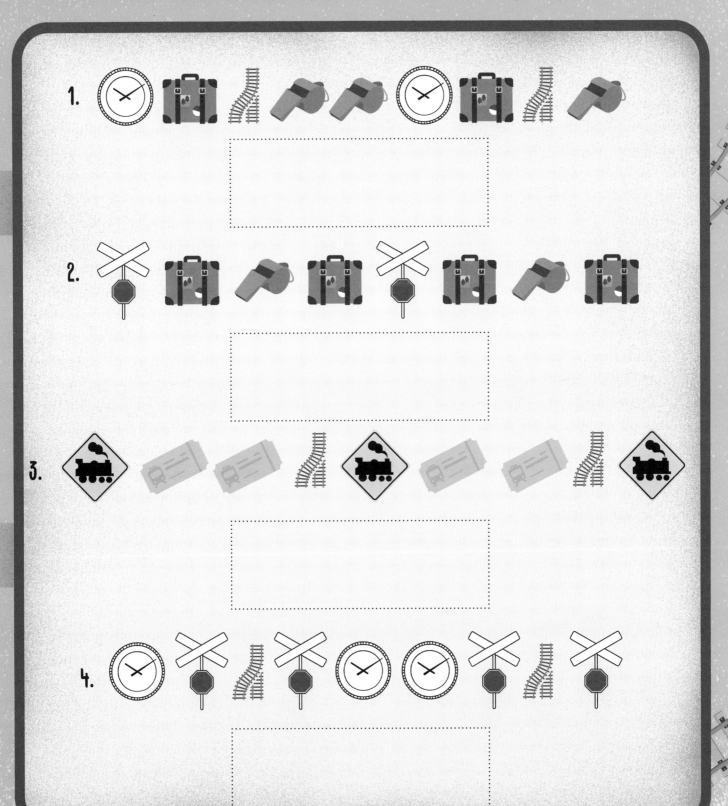

The Driver's View

Train drivers must be very observant. Study this picture for two minutes. Then cover it and answer the questions on the opposite page from memory. No peeking!

How much do you remember from the picture?
Circle your answers.

1. What speed is the train travelling at?

   A. 30 kph
   B. 60 kph
   C. 90 kph

2. What time is it?

   A. 15:30
   B. 12:00
   C. 18:45

3. What colour is the brake handle?

   A. Yellow
   B. Red
   C. Black

4. What is the name of the city?

   A. Foxbar City
   B. Boxer City
   C. Boxcar City

5. What colour is the signal light on the track?

   A. Red
   B. Yellow
   C. Green

6. What is flying in the sky?

   A. A helicopter
   B. A hot air balloon
   C. An airplane

If you score: 5–6   You are a master train driver.

3–4   You have good observation skills.

0–2   Keep practising!

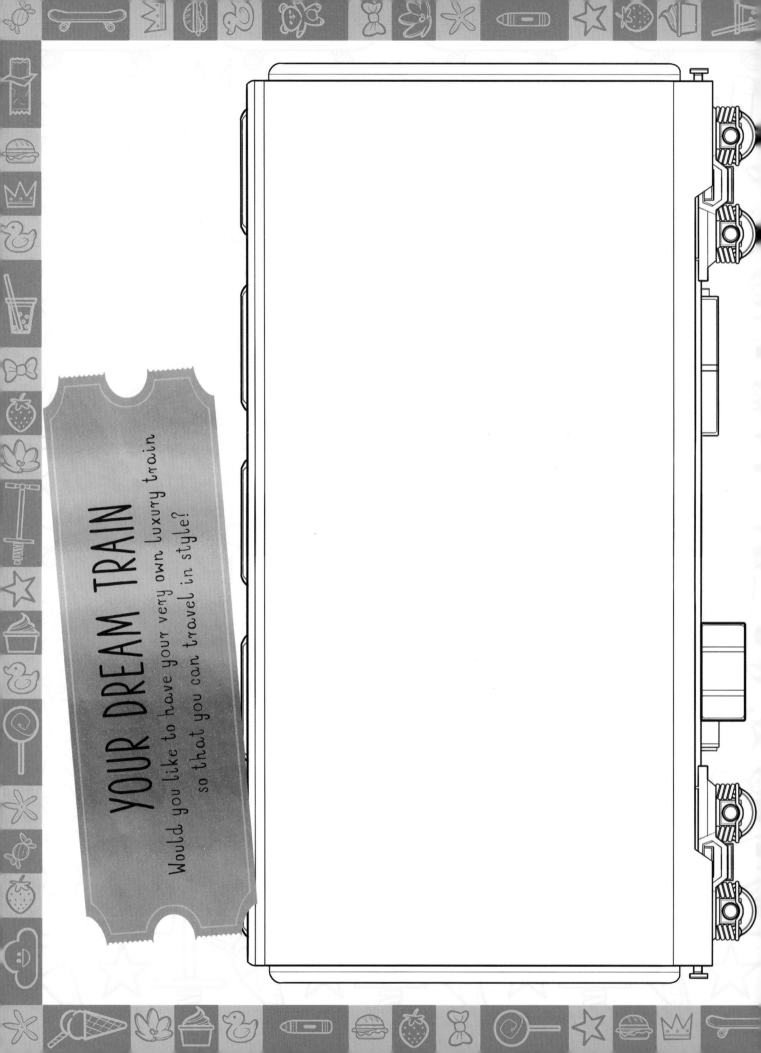

YOUR DREAM TRAIN

Would you like to have your very own luxury train
so that you can travel in style?

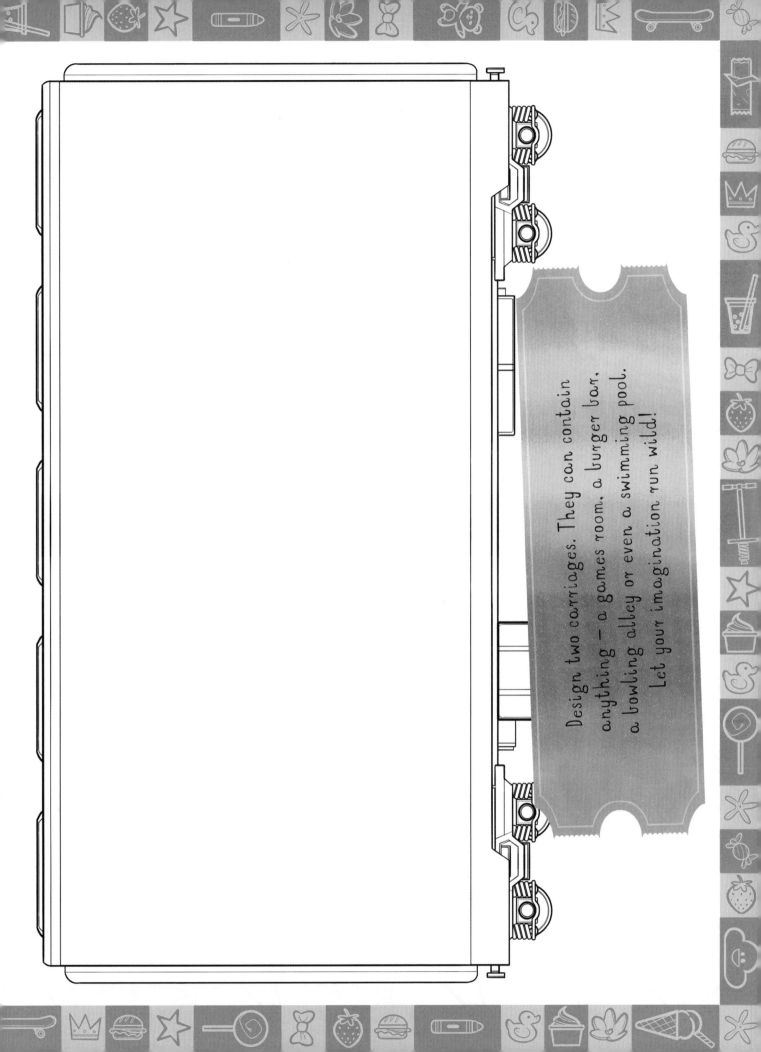

Design two carriages. They can contain anything – a games room, a burger bar, a bowling alley or even a swimming pool. Let your imagination run wild!

Trouble Onboard

You're aboard the train, excited to set off. But there's a problem. The driver's hat has been stolen! Can you use the clues to find out who took it?

- They are not wearing a tie.

- They are not wearing a hat.

- They are wearing sunglasses.

- They have black hair.

- They are not wearing shorts.

- They are not wearing purple.

Cross out the passengers as you eliminate them from your search. Circle the person who took the hat once you work out who they are.

39

A family

A shop

A sweet

A person running

A newspaper

A baby

I-Spy Game
There are many interesting sights to see at a train station. How many of these things can you see when you're out and about? Tick the box as you see each one.

A set of steps

A sandwich

A dog

A train worker

A ticket office

An information board

A person sleeping

A pair of glasses

A bird

A clock

A hot drink

Something yellow

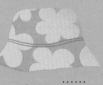
A platform sign

A suitcase

A person talking on the phone

A book

A person smiling

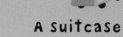
A hat

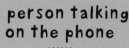

On Time

Find all of the departure times listed below in this grid. Numbers can run forwards, downwards or diagonally. Circle or highlight the numbers as you go.

2	0	1	9	3	5	6	8	3	0	0	7	1	1	4	5
3	5	7	3	8	2	9	7	3	2	5	9	0	8	6	1
1	0	5	4	6	7	0	0	2	6	1	3	7	3	2	8
0	8	5	0	8	0	0	2	0	2	5	0	0	2	1	2
8	3	1	5	9	0	9	6	2	3	7	2	6	1	0	7
1	0	0	7	3	8	5	1	4	5	1	3	8	7	3	6
2	3	6	2	8	9	4	8	3	0	5	4	2	5	8	1
1	9	2	0	3	5	0	7	1	4	2	9	5	4	2	8
3	0	8	3	0	5	0	4	8	0	0	6	1	7	5	6
8	6	7	5	6	0	9	3	9	4	8	2	0	5	9	2
2	3	1	8	7	1	2	2	1	7	1	0	6	8	0	1
0	0	8	3	1	9	4	7	9	0	0	3	4	2	8	7
1	4	5	0	6	2	9	3	5	8	6	1	7	9	2	0
0	2	0	3	9	0	4	1	8	3	9	6	5	1	7	8
3	9	2	1	5	0	6	7	3	6	2	1	0	5	1	9
0	5	4	9	8	1	9	5	9	0	1	5	3	2	0	5

Departure times

Parkville	0800		Cleetcastle	1532
Oldtown	0810		Po County	1839
Easton	0900		Dipdale	2024
Conington	1145		Peaceford	2103
Reedham	1213		Mount Bright	2359
Biffton-on-Sea	1451			

The Magic Tunnel

This game can be played alone, or with as many people as you like. Follow the prompts and fill in the blanks to create an interesting story, called 'The Magic Tunnel'. Once you've filled in all of the blanks, read your story aloud. The sillier the words you choose, the funnier the story will be!

I blinked and shook my head as the train came out of the magic

tunnel. I couldn't believe my eyes.

The sky was _____ and there were lots
(A colour)

of _____ running around.
(A type of zoo animal)

'Oh no!' I exclaimed. There was a walking, talking _____
(A type of sweet)

being chased by a _____ the size of a dog!
(A type of insect)

The train stopped at a town called _____.
(A vegetable)

A _____ dressed in a _____
(A magical creature)   (A type of costume)

came aboard and ordered everyone off the train. As I walked into

the town, I saw that the people looked very strange. They had

_____ for heads and were _____ metres tall.
(A type of fruit)   (A number
                                                          above 10)

'Hey!' I heard someone shout. I turned to see _____
(A famous singer)

standing in front of me. 'Are you hungry? I've got some lovely

_____ for you to munch on.'
(A type of clothing)

'Wow!' I said, looking at what I was offered. 'You don't actually eat

that, do you?' I gasped.

Just then, a _____ wearing a huge crown and
(A type of pet)

driving a _____ stopped right next to me.
(A type of vehicle)

'I am _____ and this is my kingdom.
(The name of someone you know)

The punishment for coming here without my permission is to have

your _____ tickled every day for a week!'
(A body part)

I ran away as fast as I could and dived back onto the

train. It pulled out of the station and sped back to

the magic tunnel. 'Phew!' I thought to myself.

'That was a lucky escape!'

what's wrong?

LOOK CLOSELY AT THIS BUSY STATION.
THERE ARE SOME THINGS HERE THAT DON'T BELONG...

CAN YOU FIND AND CIRCLE ALL EIGHT THINGS?

Logic Puzzle

Four friends each took a different toy and piece of fruit on their train journey. Can you work out who took what? Draw an 'X' in the box when you have solved each clue - one is already done for you.

	Candice	Meera	Travis	James
A banana				
A kiwi fruit				
A strawberry				
Grapes				
A book				
Blowing bubbles			X	
A teddy bear				
Crayons				

1. The toy that James took is made of wax.

2. The fruit that Travis took is covered in seeds.

3. Candice took something with a spine. Her fruit is yellow.

4. Meera took something that can be cuddled. Her fruit is furry on the outside.

So Many Shapes!

How many rectangles, triangles and circles
you can spot in the picture of this train?
Write your answers in the boxes below.

It's not as easy as you might think!
Look at the triangles at the top of the
chimney. Together, these two triangles form
a larger triangle, which makes three.

Number of rectangles _____

Number of triangles _____

Number of circles _____

Lost & Found

Railway stations have lost property offices to store items that people have misplaced while on a journey.

Above, there are four shelves of lost property.
Can you circle the odd item on each shelf?

Dressed for Work

Congratulations! You've been hired to design the logos and uniforms for a new train company.

What will you name your train company?

Colour these boxes with three colours for your train company.

Draw a symbol for your train company.

You could use an animal, your favourite food or you could create your own symbol.

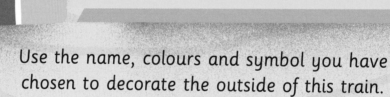

Use the name, colours and symbol you have chosen to decorate the outside of this train.

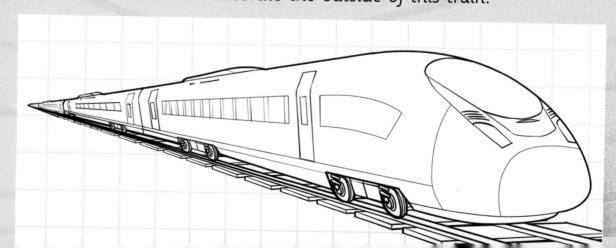

Now it's time to design the uniforms. Add colour and any extra details you'd like to the clothes below.

WHERE ARE THEY OFF TO?

People use trains for many different reasons. Look at these people waiting on the platform. Write or draw in the speech bubbles to give a reason for each of their journeys.

Can You Find?

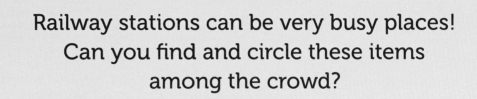

Railway stations can be very busy places!
Can you find and circle these items
among the crowd?

a camera   a pair of sunglasses   a dog
a pushchair   a bunch of flowers   a green shirt
a map   a walking stick   a suitcase
a banana

Design a Track

You're in charge of designing your own train track. Draw it however you'd like on the opposite page - it could all be joined up, or it could start in one place and end in another.

Here are some pieces of rail you could draw in your track:

Here are some extras you could add around it - or you can come up with your own:

Bridge

Tunnel

Barrier

Trees

Station

Crane

Town

Windmill

Pond

Car

Train shed

Cows

Farm

Signs

Colour-by-Numbers

Colour in all the numbered shapes using the key.
How many pieces of luggage can you find?
Write the number below.

Key

1
2
3
4
5
6
7

There are .... pieces of luggage.

PACK FOR THE JOURNEY

You are going on a long rail journey. Draw all of the items that you need to take in your backpack.

YOU NEED TO TAKE:

Your ticket

An activity

A snack

A drink

A book or
a magazine

My Day of Travel

Fill in this keepsake diary of your trip. It can be real or imaginary!

Date: _ _ _ _ _ _ _ _ _ _ _

I arrived at _ _ _ _ _ _ _ _ _ _ _ _ _ _ _ station to catch the train.

I was travelling to _ .

I travelled with _ .

Before we boarded the train, I _

_ . The train journey was _ _ _ hours.

I took some tasty snacks for the journey, including _ _ _ _ _ _ _ _ _ _ _ _ _ _ _ and _ .

I looked out of the window and I saw _ _ _ _ _ _ _ _ _ _ _ .

The weather was _ _ _ _ _ _ _ _ _ _ _ _ _ _ _ _ _ .

The train stopped in _ _ _ _ _ _ _ _ places along the way.

As we arrived at my destination, the first thing I saw

was _ .

The first three things I did when I got off the train were:

_ _

_ _

_ _ _ _ _ _ _ _ _ _ _ _ _ _ _ _

My next trip will be by:

plane/boat/bicycle/spaceship ←

Circle your choice

Signed,

_ _ _ _ _ _ _ _ _ _ _ _ _ _ _ _ _ _

59

ANSWERS

PAGE 6: SPOT THE DIFFERENCE

PAGES 8: FIND THE FREIGHT TRAIN

The matching freight train is B.

PAGE 9: DOT-TO-DOT

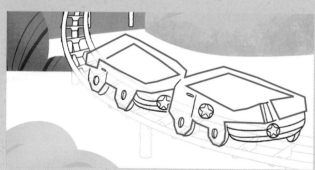

PAGE 10: BELIEVE IT OR NOT!

1. They are both the same size.
2. They are both the same size.
They are both optical illusions!

PAGE 11: FASTER THAN A SPEEDING BULLET

1. Flying Scotsman
2. The Rocket
3. Shinkansen

PAGE 12: MATCHING GAME

PAGE 13: TRAIN, PLANE OR SHIP

1. Train
2. Plane
3. Ship
4. Train
5. Plane

PAGE 16: HIDDEN TRAIN

PAGE 17: WHICH LINE?

The train that goes to the beach is B.

PAGE 18: PICTURE SUDOKU

PAGE 19: SUBWAY CONUNDRUM

The station that Bea needs to get to is Riverside.

PAGE 24: TRACK PUZZLE

1. B

2. D

3. A

4. C

PAGE 25: TRAIN TEASERS

1. It's the same amount of time.
2. The dog was travelling aboard the train.
3. The colour of your hair – you're driving the train!

PAGE 26: TRUE OR FALSE?

1. False. The Trans-Siberian Railway is 9,289 kilometres long.
2. False. On average, 3.5 million people use Tokyo's Shinjuku Station every day.
3. True

PAGE 27: CAPITAL CITIES

Berlin = Germany
Tokyo = Japan
Beijing = China
London = UK
Paris = France
Washington, D.C. = USA
Odd one out = Moscow

PAGES 30–31: SEARCH THE SLEEPER

PAGE 33: WHAT'S NEXT?

1.

2.

3.

4.

PAGES 34–35: THE DRIVER'S VIEW

1. A
2. A
3. B
4. C
5. C
6. A

PAGES 38–39: TROUBLE ONBOARD

PAGE 41: ON TIME

2	0	1	9	3	5	6	8	3	0	0	7	1	1	4	5
3	5	7	3	8	2	9	7	3	2	5	9	0	8	6	1
1	0	5	4	6	7	0	0	2	6	1	3	7	3	2	8
0	8	5	0	8	0	0	2	0	2	5	0	0	2	1	2
8	3	1	5	9	0	9	6	2	3	7	2	6	1	0	7
1	0	0	7	3	8	5	1	4	5	1	3	8	7	3	6
2	3	6	2	8	9	4	8	3	0	5	4	2	5	8	1
1	9	2	0	3	5	0	7	1	4	2	9	5	4	2	8
3	0	8	3	0	5	0	4	8	0	0	6	1	7	5	6
8	6	7	5	6	0	9	3	9	4	8	2	0	5	9	2
2	3	1	8	7	1	2	2	1	7	1	0	6	8	0	1
0	0	8	3	1	9	4	7	9	0	0	3	4	2	8	7
1	4	5	0	6	2	9	3	5	8	6	1	7	9	2	0
0	2	0	3	9	0	4	1	8	3	9	6	5	1	7	8
3	9	2	1	5	0	6	7	3	6	2	1	0	5	1	9
0	5	4	9	8	1	9	5	9	0	1	5	3	2	0	5

PAGE 44: WHAT'S WRONG?

PAGE 45: LOGIC PUZZLE

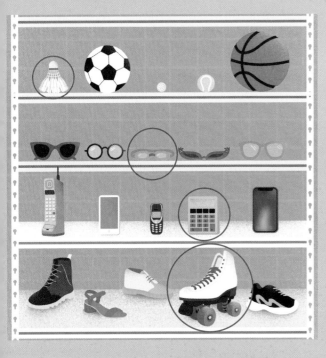

	Candice	Meera	Travis	James
A banana	X			
A kiwi fruit		X		
A strawberry			X	
Grapes				X
A book	X			
Blowing bubbles			X	
A teddy bear		X		
Crayons				X

PAGE 46: SO MANY SHAPES!

Number of rectangles = 8
Number of triangles = 8
Number of circles = 8

PAGE 47: LOST & FOUND

PAGES 52–53: CAN YOU FIND?

PAGE 56: COLOUR-BY-NUMBERS

There are five pieces of luggage.

First published in the UK in 2020 by

Ivy Kids

An imprint of The Quarto Group
The Old Brewery
6 Blundell Street
London N7 9BH
United Kingdom
www.QuartoKnows.com

British Library Cataloguing-in-Publication Data
A catalogue record for this book is available from the British Library.

ISBN: 978-1-78240-984-7

This book was conceived, designed & produced by

Ivy Kids

58 West Street, Brighton BN1 2RA, United Kingdom

PUBLISHER David Breuer
MANAGING EDITOR Susie Behar
ART DIRECTOR Hanri van Wyk
DESIGNER Kate Haynes
PROJECT EDITOR Lucy Menzies
IN-HOUSE EDITOR Hannah Dove
EXTERNAL DESIGNER Elise Gaignet

Manufactured in Guangdong, China TT012020

1 3 5 7 9 10 8 6 4 2